Contents

5

8

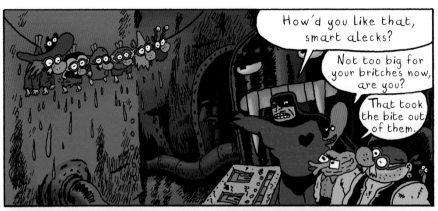

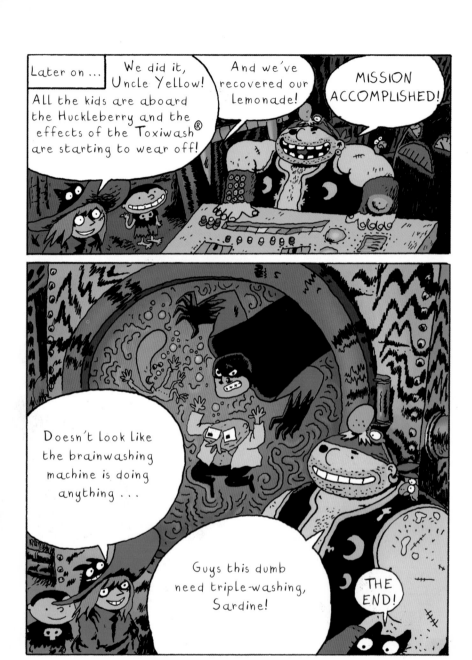

12

14

No, Sardine, you don't understand. This poor guy's been bitten by a CHA-CHA fly.

A Cha-Cha fly?

CHA, CHA, CHACHACHA I LIKE YOUR GROOVE

The Cha-Cha fly has a terrible bite, kids.

Does it itch a lot?

AND YOU LIKE MY GROOVE AND YOU ARE SO SMOOTH

No, Little Louie, it's much worse! Once you've been bitten, you get stupid dance tunes stuck in your head and you can't get them out!

AND YOU LIKE MY GROOVE CUZ I AM SO SMOOTH

And this one's skipping on top of it. Where's that club, Sardine?

Here, Uncle Yellow.

OOH I LIKE YOUR BAM!

AAH!

There ... Now he'll rest for a few minutes.

And so will we!

YUM! Come look!

Look—crunch!—someone dropped a whole bunch of chocolate truffles! ... YUM!

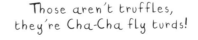

Those aren't truffles, they're Cha-Cha fly turds!

BLECK! YUCK!

HA! HA! HA!

Cha-Cha flies live in cocoa trees. They use their delicious chocolate turds to lure their victims to them.

Gross! But delicious ...

17

25

26

Meanwhile, in outer space...

I don't understand, Krok. He should have been here hours ago. Do you think he forgot about me?

Don't worry, Supermuscleman. Here, put on your robe. It's getting chilly.

Do you think he came and we didn't hear him? Maybe he thought no one was home so he left.

No, he would've drunk the hot chocolate you left out for him. The cup's still full!

Maybe he just doesn't like me anymore.

Knock! Knock! Knock!

KROK! THAT'S HIM!!

There he is!

29

31

32

But it just scares everyone away instead!

Not us!

Being lonely for so long has made me mean. It's especially bad on New Year's Eve, when everyone else is having fun. Now I just eat to forget how sad I am!

So you'd stop causing trouble for the universe if you had some friends?

Yes, that's all I want!

OK, then listen to me. Can you make your big-mouth ship smile?

Yes, but it's been a long time since I've tried.

Here's what you're going to do: give away your caviar, your champagne, and your oysters to anyone in the galaxy who doesn't have any of their own. And SMILE while you do it!

OK.

When you're done, you can come find us at our Grammy's house. We'll save some cake for you.

GREAT! I'LL write down the address!

Later, at Grammy's house...

That's the doorbell!

It must be Bobby!

Let's go see.

Later that night . . .

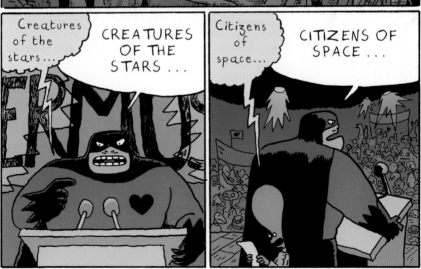

46

47

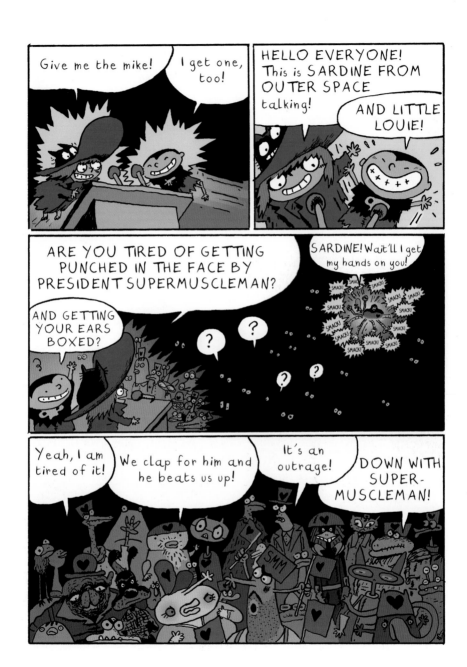

Ah, it was before your time. People were crazy about her in the old days. Her star used to shine brighter than all the others.

But she never leaves her big Follywood mansion anymore. Everyone's forgotten all about her except for me!

That's so sad.

Now Follywood's light is growing dim, and soon it will be cold and gray if I don't do something about it!

So, why'd you try to rob us?

I . . . I want to plate Follywood with gold. Then it will shine just as brightly as before, and Ava Garbo will love me!

Well, you came to the wrong place. We're broke!

55

You have so much gold that I can't even count it all, and there isn't enough room for it on the ship!

Let's buy some weapons and start a war!

No, no, you should save your money. But we have to find a way to store it all! I have a new invention that just might do the trick!

Tell me ...

I've melted your gold down and made it into a paste that takes up much less space. Then I squeezed it into these gold tubes!

With this invention, we can fit twice as much gold in here, no problem. And look, your safe is far from being full!

Ava Garbo? Why, she hasn't lived here for years! My name is Janine.

Ja...Janine?

What the heck did you do to my star? It's much too bright! I'm old, you know, and my eyes are tired!

Er...I thought...I mean...

Mister Andy thought you were tired of living in this big mansion all by yourself.

So he wants to invite you to come live with him on his little satellite. It'll be perfect for the two of you. Right, Mister Andy?

Er...well, I mean... yes...

62

The flea circus would like to thank Yellow Shoulder, Sardine, and Little Louie for coming out . . .

WATCH OUT!

WATCH OUT! IT'S DUNDERHEAD!

Oh, no!

EVERYONE HIDE!! THERE'S A DUNDERHEAD COMING!

What's a Dunderhead, Uncle Yellow Shoulder?

Let's go and see . . .

68

71

You've gotta understand. I don't have anything against you, I'm just so bored in this lighthouse!

Have you tried sliding down the banisters?

Yeah, like a million times. It's no fun anymore. You space pirates are so lucky—you get to travel all over the universe!

Yeah, we are!

I'm pretty lonely here. My mom's all right, but the lighthouse takes up all her time.

STUPID LIGHTHOUSE!

That's sad . . .

I have an idea!

79

LATER...

MEANWHILE, ON PLANET BUBULINA ...

Tonight is HOT HOT HOT on 103 FM!

103 FM, your number one station for shivers, shakes, aches, and pains ...

And runny noses!

And now, a little music for Sardine!

AAAH!

Supermuscleman, take off your head-phones!

Wha . . . what was that music?

It's a one-man band! He can hit a pan with a fork, grind his teeth, snort like a pig, and crack his knuckles, all at once.

It's awful . . .

Sardine will really hate it!

And that's not all! Follow me . . .

Krok, this plan to poison Sardine's dreams is absolutely perfect!

Heh heh!

These are the Channel 103 TV studios, Supermuscleman!

THE TELEVIRUS!

103 TV apologizes for this temporary break in programming . . .

88

90

AAAAH!

Here, Sardine, drink this lemon tea!

Lemon tea? How come?

Well...because you have a fever...

Not anymore I don't! I want ice cream!...

...and lots of kitty treats. He really deserves them!

MRRR...

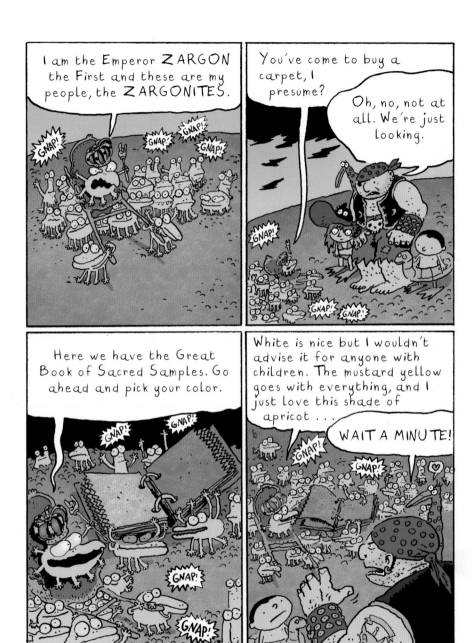

95

You know, Uncle Yellow, it would be nice to have a carpet . . . at least in our bedroom.

I said NO, Sardine!

Well, can we sleep on this blue carpet tonight, anyway?

Ooh, can we, Captain? It's so fluffy and soft!

Weeeell . . . All right. We'll leave in the morning.

Sleep tight, kids. I'll keep one eye open in case Zargon tries any funny business.

Make sure it's your good eye, Uncle Yellow!

If I catch Zargon the First, I'll crush him between my little toes!

THE NEXT MORNING AT DAWN...

Little Louie, wake up! Uncle Yellow's gone!

Hmph?

I've looked everywhere, I've called for him . . . but he doesn't answer! The Zargonites must have kidnapped him!

Really? How'd they do it?

Scrtch! Scrtch!

It doesn't matter! Come on! We need equipment so we can exterminate those little bugs!

We have lots of weapons for fighting big monsters, but there's nothing for microbes!

I have an idea!

SNAP!

MEANWHILE . . .

Where in space am I?

HA! HA!

GNAP!

GNAP!

GNAP!

GNAP! GNAP!

GNAP!

98

100

Who are you anyway?

I'm the Ice Watcher. I'm the one who keeps an eye on your ice cream and space yogurt while you're sleeping.

Not long ago, two guys broke into the fridge. They took me by surprise, tied me up, and stole all your dairy products before escaping.

Ah! What pigs!

We'll get them, though! Their ship must have a leak—it's leaving a trail of milk behind. All we have to do is follow it.

What a waste! With all the little aliens who are starving!

108

AAAHH!!
THE MILK! IT'S TURNING!

KA-PLOSH

Barf!

LATER . . .

You like tying people up, HUH?! Well, now it's your turn!!

GRR!

Let's go, Sardine! We'll take a spin around the Milky Way and get rid of all those awful toll booths. No one should have to pay for milk!

You're so dumb, Sardine!

What do you fish-ish for?

We fish-ish for st-stars.

Then we se-sell them to the arm-my.

They use them to decorate the sold-diers.

WHAT?!

You're robbing the universe of its beautiful stars in order to decorate your generals?

Well, yeah. It's our jo-job.

They pa-pay us for it.

And who pays you?

President Sup-per . . .

...SUPER-MUSCLE-MAN?

Tha-that's the one!

MEANWHILE, ON THE SPACE STATION "KEEL"...

Supermuscleman, sir, I'd like to introduce you to our new commando team, Code Name Whippit. They just graduated from our military academy.

They're specially trained in combat against little children.

Good work, boys!

GLORY TO YOU, SUPERMUSCLEMAN!

118

120

First Second

New York & London

Copyright © 2001 by Bayard Editions Jeunesse
English translation copyright © 2006 by First Second

Published by First Second
First Second is an imprint of Roaring Brook Press, a division of Holtzbrinck
Publishing Holdings Limited Partnership
175 Fifth Avenue, New York, NY 10010

Distributed in the United Kingdom by Macmillan Children's Books, a division
of Pan Macmillan.

Originally published in France in 2001 under the titles *La machine à laver la cervelle*
and *Les voleurs de yaourts* by Bayard Editions Jeunesse, Paris

Design by Danica Novgorodoff

Library of Congress Cataloging-in-Publication Data

Guibert, Emmanuel.
Sardine in outer space / Emmanuel Guibert and Joann Sfar ; translated by Sasha Watson ;
colorist, Walter Pezzali ; letterer, François Batet.-- 1st American ed.
p. cm.
Translations of stories originally published separately in French.
ISBN: 978-1-59643-126-3 (v.1)
ISBN: 978-1-59643-127-0 (v.2)

1. Graphic novels. I. Sfar, Joann. II. Title.
PN6747.G85A2 2006
741.5'944--dc22
2005021790

First Second books are available for special promotions and premiums.
For details, contact: Director of Special Markets, Holtzbrinck Publishers.

First American Edition September 2006

Printed in China by South China Printing Co. Ltd., Dongguan City, Guangdong Province

7 9 10 8